In The Pink

JIM DAVIS

RAVETTE BOOKS

First published by Ravette Books Limited 1987
Reprinted 1987 (twice)
This edition first published 1988
Reprinted 1988, 1989

Printed and bound in Great Britain
for Ravette Books Limited,
3 Glenside Estate, Star Road, Partridge Green,
Horsham, West Sussex RH13 8RA
by Cox & Wyman Ltd, Reading

ISBN 0 948456 67 1

© 1986 United Feature Syndicate, Inc.

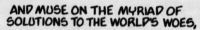

© 1986 United Feature Syndicate, Inc.

GARFIELD'S Believe it, or DON'T!

A JON ARBUCKLE CLAIMS TO OWN A CAT WHO CAN EAT 10 TIMES ITS BODY WEIGHT. TO VERIFY HIS CLAIM WE OFFERED THE CAT 270 POUNDS OF LASAGNA

© 1986 United Feature Syndicate, Inc.

THE CAT ATE ONLY 219 POUNDS OF LASAGNA

THINGS WENT SO WELL IN REHEARSAL

Believe it, or DON'T!

JIM DAVIS

1-21

© 1986 United Feature Syndicate, Inc.

© 1986 United Feature Syndicate, Inc.

THE TV ADVERTISERS DIDN'T WASTE ANY TIME

© 1986 United Feature Syndicate, Inc.

I'VE BEEN ON A DIET ONE DAY AND THEY'RE ALREADY RUNNING MORE FOOD COMMERCIALS

3-19

HERE'S YOUR DIET SALAD, GARFIELD

3-25

WOULD YOU LIKE ANYTHING ON IT?

IF YOU DON'T MIND

© 1986 United Feature Syndicate, Inc.

PERHAPS YOU COULD GARNISH IT WITH A CHOCOLATE CAKE

JIM DAVPS

GARFIELD'S

Believe it,
or DON'T !

A CAT IN LUBBOCK, TEXAS
GAVE BIRTH TO 57 KITTENS

© 1986 United Feature Syndicate, Inc.

WHEN ASKED HOW SHE FELT
AFTER GIVING BIRTH TO
QUINSEPTUPLETS, SHE SAID:

I'LL FEEL BETTER
WHEN THEY START
SLEEPING THROUGH
THE NIGHT

JIM DAVIS 1-25

Believe it,
or DON'T !

© 1986 United Feature Syndicate, Inc.

JIM DAVIS

8-11

© 1986 United Feature Syndicate, Inc.

8-12   JIM DAVIS

© 1986 United Feature Syndicate, Inc.

THIS LOOKS LIKE A NICE PLACE...

© 1986 United Feature Syndicate, Inc.

FOR A NAP

JIM DAVIS 11-21

© 1986 United Feature Syndicate, Inc.

© 1986 United Feature Syndicate, Inc.

© 1986 United Feature Syndicate, Inc.

OTHER GARFIELD BOOKS IN THIS SERIES

LANDSCAPE SERIES

COLOUR TV SPECIALS

COLOUR TREASURIES

The Second Garfield Treasury	£5.95
The Third Garfield Treasury	£5.95
The Fourth Garfield Treasury	£5.95
Garfield A Weekend Away	£4.95
Garfield How To Party	£3.95
Garfield Book Of Cat Names	£2.50
Garfield Best Ever	£4.95
Garfield Easter Bunny	£3.95

All these books are available at your local bookshop or newsagent, or can be ordered direct from the publisher. Just tick the titles you require and fill in the form below. Prices and availability subject to change without notice.

Ravette Books Limited, 3 Glenside Estate, Star Road, Partridge Green, Horsham, West Sussex RH13 8RA

Please send a cheque or postal order and allow the following for postage and packing. UK: Pocket-books – 45p for up to two books and 15p for each additional book. Landscape Series, TV Specials and Garfield Book of Cat Names – 45p for one book plus 15p for each additional book. Treasuries, Garfield A Weekend Away, Garfield How To Party, Garfield Best Ever and Garfield Easter Bunny – 75p for each book.

Name ....

Address ....

....